SPLOTCH
and SPLAT!

Rocio Bonilla

Hello!

My name is LEO and this is my friend MAGGIE. We're wearing our painting smocks because...

We love painting!

We paint lots of things we see, like animals, skies, flowers AND THINGS THAT WE MAKE UP, TOO.

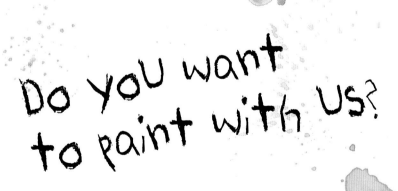

Do you want to paint with us?

A lot of colours!

We'll be using all types of art materials, like pencils, crayons, watercolours, poster paints and markers...

as well as scissors, glue and some old newspaper so we don't make a mess!

Why don't you put on a
PAINTING SMOCK OR APRON? NOW...

Let's get going!

ONE-COLOUR SPLOTCHES

We'll start with a game!
I'll paint a splotch of colour and then you think about what it could be and finish the drawing.

It's such good FUN!

Pink watercolour

A pink splotch...

4

Mmm...it's easy, isn't it?

An ear...
Four legs...
A tail...
And a trunk!

Ta da!

Crayon

I FOUND AN ELEPHANT
HIDDEN IN THE **splotch!**

5

I know you're going to say that elephants aren't pink, right? It doesn't matter, because that's what makes creativity fun. Let your imagination go wild and invent loads of things. It is like doing magic!
Let's try it again.

WE'RE GOING TO PAINT MORE ANIMALS!

This time, I'll make the splotch, okay?

GREEN!

What could it be?

It can be so many different things

Okaaaaay

LET'S SEE WHAT ANIMAL YOU CAN FIND HERE...

even greener?

It looks like a PEAR...

Now let's try BLUE...

This is my
KITTEN →

HER NAME IS

MAISIE

13

Oh, Maisieee...!

WhooPS!

Maggie tripped and the pot of paint went flying.

What a big puddle...

Hmm...
so, now
we need
a really
big idea!

Easy...

JUST THE THING!

HA-HA... THE DRIPS GAVE ME A GOOD IDEA!

19

Gosh, that splotch is very

strange

Oh... what shall I do with all these small splotches?

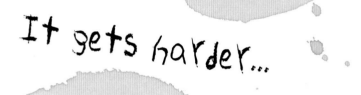

It gets harder...

...all the time!

Can you think of something?

21

I know... a **bear!**

AND WHAT DO BEARS LIKE TO EAT?

The honey that bees make!

Me too...

Leo, let's make
a really humungous...

coloured splotch...

Wow! PURPLE!

25

DON'T FORGET THE
little details

26

HOW ABOUT SOME ORANGE SPLOTCHES?

28

And now...

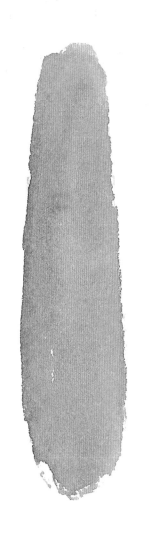

the last one!

We painted in...

Two more splotches!

31

Now it's
YOUR tUrn!

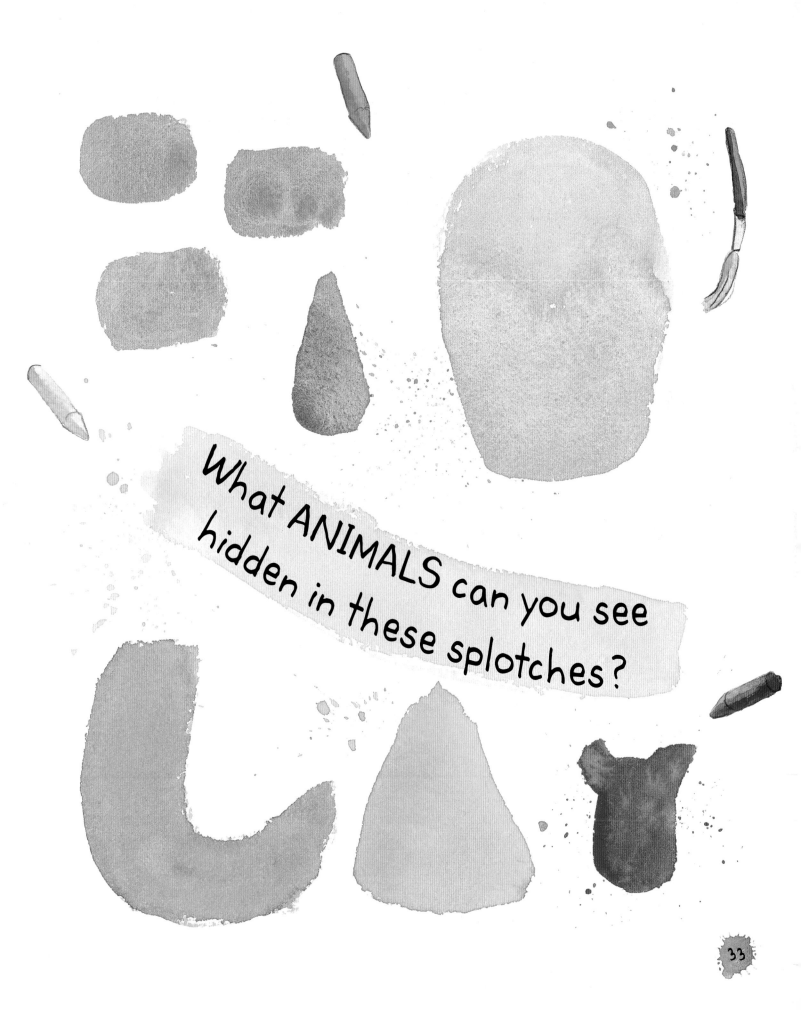

What ANIMALS can you see hidden in these splotches?

Excellent!

What GREAT IDEAS!
You're a STAR at finding animals hidden in SPLOTCHES.

Shall we continue?

OBSERVE and then IMAGINE...

Hasn't it been fun using

your imagination for drawing?

To be really creative, it's
important for us

TO NURTURE
OUR CREATIVITY

Think about a toy dog with batteries that make him walk
and bark.

Woof woof!

If the batteries run out and we forget to replace them, the dog stops moving and barking, right?

The same thing happens with our creativity.

WE NEED TO FEED IT

so it keeps working!

We have to eat well to grow bigger and stronger, right?

Well, the more we nourish our creativity,

the bigger it becomes too!

So, how can we feed our imaginations?

The best way to do it is to OBSERVE
our surroundings to DISCOVER
things that we can USE FOR INSPIRATION.

LET'S TRY IT OUT

We're going to draw a tree!

Make your tree HOWEVER YOU LIKE, with paints
or markers, pencils or brushes.

This one's mine.

And that one's mine.

Have you ever noticed that we almost always draw trees THE SAME WAY? Round and green, with a brown trunk.

However, if we go to the PARK, or walk in the WOODS

we can see that trees are...

Red coloured...

Triangular...

Hanging...

Yellow coloured...

Orange coloured...

Sometimes with no leaves...

Sometimes with blossom... and... **Even pink trees!**

There are so many different trees with so many different

colours and shapes!

I'm using coloured pencils!

What fabulous trees!
And now...

43

This is our MAGIC

Are you ready

FOREST

to try it yourself now?

What about
adding some

Ready!

plants?

Wait Leo, you're forgetting
something! Before drawing,
let's go and...

OBSERVE

Look!

Plants aren't only green...

There are RED leaves... GREY leaves...

And even ones with spots!

Imagine

that we have some empty pots.
Let's fill them with our SPLOTCHES!

LOOK: THESE PLANTS HAVE STRIPES AND PATTERNS.

And some plants even gobble up flies!

And don't forget about the Shapes!

Pointy ones...

Long ones...

Be careful! That one's spikey!

AND THIS ONE IS
LIKE THE HORNS
OF A REINDEER!

Shall we paint the POTS?

THOSE POOR PLANTS LOOK AS THOUGH THEY'RE STARVING...

We are!

And if we add some

FLOWERS

TO OUR GARDEN?

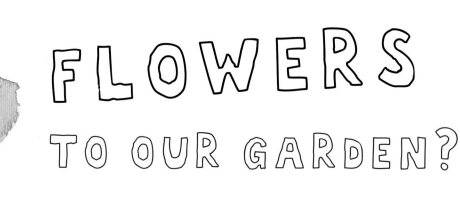

I love flowers!

Shouldn't we observe them first?

Round LIKE scoops of ICE-CREAM...

LOOK!

Long, like feathers...

and bell-shaped...

A blue flower?

HOW BEAUTIFUL!

THESE LOOK LIKE STRIPEY ICE-LOLLIES!

AND THESE ARE THE SAME COLOUR AS...

CUPCAKES!

These are RED like a butterfly...

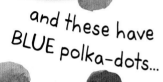

and these have BLUE polka-dots...

These are SOFT like cotton balls...

And there are even more!
Look around to see how many different flowers there are!

What do YOU think?

Should we practise our splotches and draw a BIG GARDEN?

You can almost smell them!

59

Now you can start painting yours!
But first...

SOME TIPS

1- Start the drawing with POSTER PAINTS or WATERCOLOURS and paint a lot of splotches.

2 - Let the paint DRY completely.

3 - Now you can add more details
with COLOURED PENCILS or CRAYONS.
You can also add new splotches.

4 - It doesn't matter if some splotches
OVERLAP others, in fact, it will be more
fun and the result will look more natural.

5. Use dark-coloured pencils over the light-coloured splotches and light-coloured pencils on the darker splotches. That will make your doodles stand out more.

6. Use every colour you feel like using and, above all,

have fun!

Shall we continue?

Paint everything
you want with

Splotches

and

DOODLES

using all the

colours

63

Well... Now we know how to paint with coloured splotches and we've also learned to feed our creativity so that it's always ready.

We've made

ANIMALS
TREES
PLANTS
FLOWERS

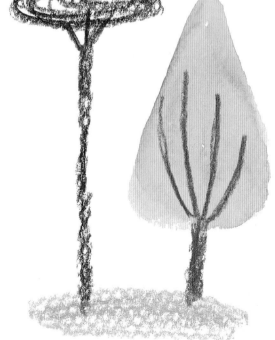

What else could we

DRAW?

A good way to get started is to think about things
that you like and enjoy. Mmm, how about...

WE CAN DRAW THEM IN

cakes!

every colour imaginable.

So get your paints ready
and LET'S GO!

Yum,
yum,
yum!

Start with WATERCOLOUR SPLOTCHES

Remember to let them dry well.

THEN ADD YOUR DOODLES

with pencils or crayons, or even make more splotches.

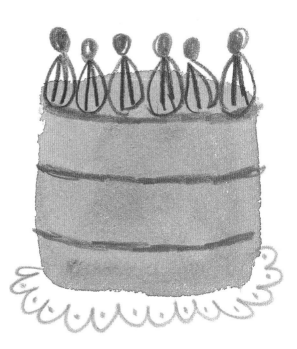

Don't forget to draw in a PLATE!

Should we do CUPCAKES now?

67

we can DRAW
THE PAPER CASES,

just like we did with
the plant pots. Then we'll add
our colour splotches.

The cases can be different shapes

Now add doodles!

Mmmm...

I could eat them all!

We love looking at the Moon and the stars.

Sometimes at night, we look out the window

AND IMAGINE STRANGE
PLANETS AND THE PEOPLE WHO
LIVE ON THEM.

Shall we draw them?

What a great idea!

Now we've had lots of practice being creative, we can easily use our imagination to make things up.
These are our

imaginary

PLANETS

This is planet LOLLIPOP

Not all aliens are green

Ours are MULTICOLOURED!
On planet Chicken Pox,
they have trunks like elephants
and red spots like their planet.

AND THEY
WEAR GLASSES
LIKE MAGGIE

74

On planet Forest, the inhabitants have LONG NECKS so they can see above the treetops.

On planet Lollipop, they are always happy because the whole planet is
made out of sugar.

The Lollipopians only have ONE EYE, DOG EARS, FOUR FEET AND RED TONGUES from eating so many lollipops.

These are our imaginary planets and their inhabitants. Now it's your turn!

SO GET YOUR PAINTS AND
PENCILS READY AND
START IMAGINING WHAT YOURS
WILL BE LIKE!

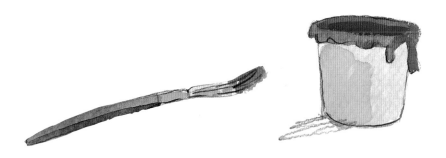

The sky is so beautiful at night, full of twinkling stars. I just love it!

But what about the sky during the day? It's really cool, too!

Remember – the sky isn't always blue. It can be many different colours, and there are all sorts of clouds, too. You just have to observe it at different times of day, in different seasons...

You'll see!

FOR EXAMPLE, THE SKY CAN BE PINK WHEN THE SUN IS SETTING.
Ooooh, that's true!

Sometimes the sky can turn golden like the SUN...

I like the sky when it's raining

because I can splash in the puddles!

But... there are also blue skies!

And there are such a lot of things in the sky we
can draw with our SPLOTCHES AND DOODLES.

Balloons...

Aeroplanes...

Helicopters...

I CAN THINK OF
SOMETHING ELSE...

Colourful clouds?

More balloons?

WHAT COULD IT BE?

Birds!

Large

Medium

Ha, ha!

Small

What about having birds in our garden?

YES, BUT WE'LL NEED INSECTS, TOO. SHALL WE **DRAW** THEM?

To paint bugs, I'm going to teach you a

TRICK

1· Choose one or more colours that you like and draw A BIG SPLOTCH that takes up a whole piece of paper.

2· Now take your pencils or crayons and DRAW STRIPES, DOTS, SCRIBBLES or whatever you like.

The idea is for the paper to be like a

pattern on a dress or shirt.

3.

Now, turn your paper over to the white side and draw some bug shapes. Carefully CUT THEM OUT. They can be:

Long

Round

Pointed

4. Glue each bug shape onto a sheet of paper. Leave spaces between them.

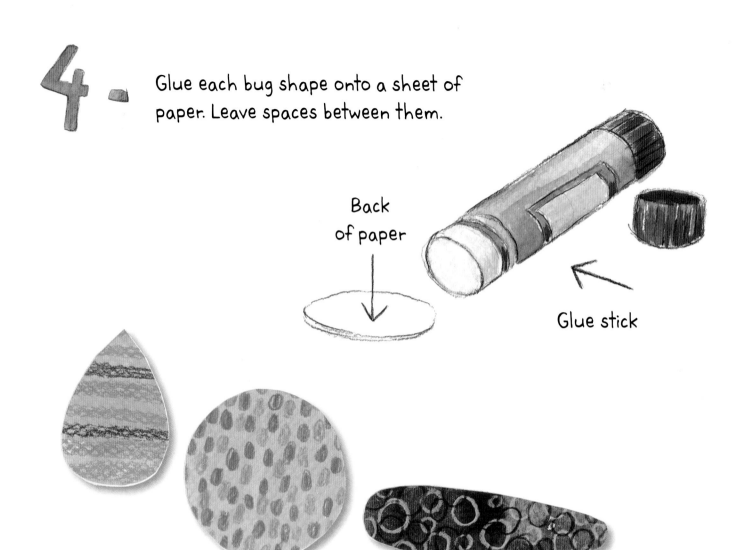

Back of paper

Glue stick

Look how pretty THEY'VE TURNED OUT!

5. Now all we need to add are the BUGS' EYES, ANTENNAE, WINGS AND LEGS.

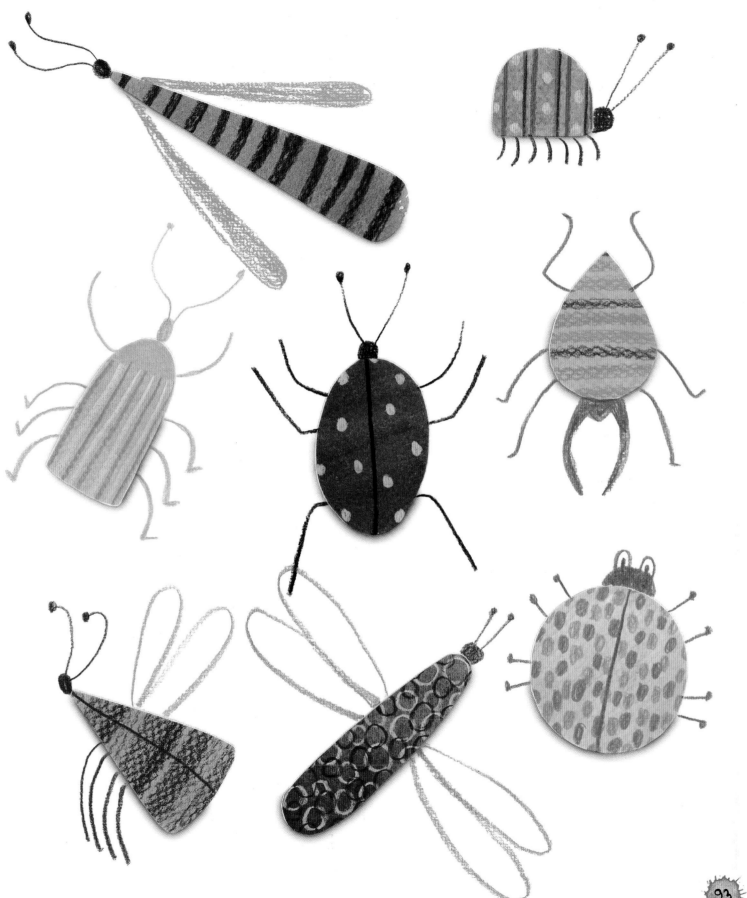

Did you enjoy that?

We've all learned to draw a ton of things and we've developed our imaginations with splotches, doodles and a few added tricks.

BUT, THE MOST IMPORTANT THING IS FOR YOU TO KEEP BEING CREATIVE...

forever!

Observe your surroundings, feed your creativity and you will never stop drawing and painting!

See you soon!

Glossary

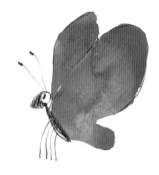

MARKER: A broad-tipped felt-tip pen.

OCTOPUS: Sea creature with eight legs that have suckers on them to help it grab things.

CRAYONS: A stick made from coloured chalk or wax that can be used for drawing.

PENCIL: A tool used for sketching and writing.

HELICOPTER: A type of aircraft that uses spinning rotor blades to fly.

PLANET: A large body of solids, liquids or gases orbiting a star.

POSTER PAINTS: A type of opaque paint used for posters.

REINDEER: A type of deer with large antlers that are often used to draw sleds.

SMOCK: A coatlike piece of clothing worn to protect the clothes underneath.

WATERCOLOUR: A type of paint thinned with water. It has a see-through look.